TRACTORS IN FOCUS
VETERAN – VINTAGE – CLASSIC – MODERN

PETER LOVE

HALSGROVE

Title page: Author Peter Love seen on Rodney Broadley's 1965 Ford Pre Force 5000 in May 2012, a type of tractor of which Peter has plenty of experience, from his working days on the spanners. Peter was presented by the NTET with the 'The Eric Middleton Cup' for services to the preservation movement in the early 1990s.

First published in Great Britain in 2012

British Library Cataloguing-in-Publication Data
A CIP record for this title is available from the British Library

ISBN 978 0 85704 174 6

HALSGROVE
Halsgrove House,
Ryelands Business Park,
Bagley Road, Wellington, Somerset TA21 9PZ
Tel: 01823 653777   Fax: 01823 216796
email: sales@halsgrove.com

Part of the Halsgrove group of companies.
Information on all Halsgrove titles is available at: www.halsgrove.com

Printed in China by Everbest Printing Co Ltd

FOREWORD

I was surprised and honoured to be asked to write the forword to Peter Love's latest book on tractors. It is a great pleasure to contribute to the work of a very good friend of mine. Peter is probably this country's leading light on the subject and his knowledge is unsurpassed. He was the founding editor of the renowned *Tractor & Machinery* magazine and I well remember working with him on the early issues. He now edits *Old Tractor* to a high standard.

Tractors and crawlers are regarded by some as the 'poor relations' of the preservation world, yet we must not forget the immeasurable part they have played in the world's economy over the past hundred years. From the basic early machines to modern 'mega' tractors, they have all changed the face of agriculture dramatically.

Restoring a tractor that is well past its 'sell-by' date can be a real challenge. I take my hat off to those people who can turn what appears to be a pile of scrap into a gleaming machine that often is better than new, and is once more capable of doing an honest day's work. Each tractor featured in this book has a story to tell — if only they could talk!

This book is a showcase for Peter's excellent photography, and features a wonderful collection of some 150 pictures that he has taken all over the world of tractors and crawlers of all sorts and in various stages of preservation. Veteran, vintage and classic machines are all covered in some detail, together with the popular and thriving sales scene. Peter's keen sense of detail provides a thorough background to each photograph.

This selection of pictures has been carefully chosen to reflect the variety found in the world of preserved tractors, and is supported by an authoritative and readable text. I commend this book to all tractor enthusiasts, and hope it achieves the success it deserves.

Richard Wade
June 2012

I dedicate this book to the memory of the late John Moffit CBE, to whom I am indebted in many ways. John was a pioneer preservationist himself through the Hunday Collection. He is seen with his son Peter at the excellent 19 September 2006 Bedfordshire Steam Engine Preservation Society's Bedfordshire Steam & Country Fayre. John is standing in front of the 1903 Ivel 131. In his last days John raised over £120,000 for charity from a historic road run with the Ivel, which is still in the family's ownership today.

WELCOME!

It was a great pleasure to receive a call from Halsgrove Publishing, telling me they wanted a tractor book. Time was short for this project and they suggested I was the man who could come up with the goods, well here it is!

Based on the theme of the four seasons, I have featured just some of the pictures I have taken during 2011 and so far in 2012. As a professional transport/agricultural journalist and photographer, I am taking pictures 52 weeks of the year and am rarely without my camera, just in case I see something of interest in the fields and on the roads. I always try to stop, but time constraints don't always allow it.

I was born into a family of transport photographers, with my late father W S Love starting in 1945 and his brother just a few years later. Dark rooms and black and white pictures were all part of daily life. In fact I bought my first camera, a 120 box job, in 1962 at the age of ten from a 'Bill Horton jumble sale' in Tonbridge, Kent and from that very first roll of film, which dad developed I had my first picture published. This was of a former SECR Stirling O1 0-6-0 tender locomotive on Tonbridge turntable in the rain.

From there I saved my gift money to buy a Brownie 127, which cost a Guinea at the time, to be followed in 1965 by uncle's Ensign, bellows and all. It had a fixed lens, but took great pictures, which father again developed. With this I took my now famous motor-cycling paddock pictures and many a bus, steam traction engine, tractor and plant picture along the way. I then ended up with a little Zeiss camera, which I didn't have much luck with, and I became disillusioned with my work.

Eventually my interest returned, I bought my first SLR 35mm camera from Pentax and I have never looked back. I became a Canon man in the '80s and have been that way ever since, besides having great success with a Pentax 645 medium format camera that I used exclusively for front magazine covers and centre spreads. I even took the bulky machine to North America on more than one occasion. The pictures taken here come from a Canon EOS 5D Mk2 and EOS 7D, using a number of lenses.

I don't class my photography as being anything that special, but I do work at trying to understand shadow and light situations. Many of the pictures here are not set up, I just don't work that way, but I have adapted the situations to the best advantage. These days digital photography has given new options to everyone; however none of the pictures used in the book have been put into Photoshop or anything similar.

Some ask, how did I become a magazine editor and jointly create the largest circulation antique tractor magazine in the world, when I have a mechanical, not academic, background. Well I was just two when I was placed on the footplate of steam road locomotive 1900 Aveling & Porter 4561 LC6 Jimmy in 1954 at Horsmonden, Kent, while father had the engine in steam. In fact this same engine is featured in Paul Stratford's *Tractor Engines: Preservation and Power* book, also published by Halsgrove, on page 29.

I have to say the engine looked rather different then, with the smaller front wheels which it worked with for 98 per cent of its working life, it being used in the threshing business. At a similar period I ended up being driven around the orchard, part of the family farm at Paddock Wood, Kent, on a 1944 Fordson Standard N Utility tractor. So, I suppose, my interest in all things transport became embedded in me at an early age and has stayed with me for all of my sixty years.

In the early '90s the tractor hobby was bubbling away and a club magazine I created and produced called *The Agriculturalist* drew the attention of Gordon Wright of Kelsey Publishing. He asked if I would create an antique tractor magazine. This was in 1994 and *Tractor & Machinery* was born, which I edited until 2007. During that period I went on to create *Classic & Vintage Commercials*, *Classic Tractor*, *Old Tractor*, *Ford and Fordson Tractors*, *Classic Plant & Machinery* and the sadly missed *Steam Traction Engine*, which was cut off before it really got going well. After my split with Kelsey in 2007 I went off to mainly work for Mortons Media and helped redevelop their *Tractor* magazine.

However, I was invited back by Kelsey Publishing and today edit *Old Tractor, Ford and Fordson Tractors*; I am editor at large on *Classic Massey and Ferguson Enthusiast*, *Classic Plant & Machinery*, and sales correspondent for *Tractor & Machinery*. I also compile the *T&M Price Guide*, which gives a full A-Z of veteran, vintage, classic tractor prices, including details of what is up and what is down, each month. It's the most comprehensive guide of its type in the world.

Besides this, I'm an *Old Glory* magazine correspondent, covering steam and other aspects of vehicle preservation. In my spare time I have columns in various other magazines including *Classic Motor Monthly* with Commercial Break and Love Steam being regular features. But that's not all; in 1996 I created the Tractor & Machinery Holiday Club, with Rob Rushen-Smith as tour manager. We took people all around the world looking at tractors, steam, trucks, scenery and much more.

In 2007 I and my wife Jayne created P & J Tours and have continued to provide similar tours to locations in the UK, Republic of Ireland, France, Holland, Germany, New Zealand and regularly to North America. We also bring groups from other countries to the UK and Republic of Ireland, as was the case in 2012 when the National Vintage Tractor Club of Norway came to the UK for a P & J tour in Yorkshire, Lancashire and Derbyshire. We also arrange Away Days to tractor factories and private collections. Further details are available from Jayne Love, tel: 01323 833125.

All that is left to say is I hope you enjoy this very small selection of my digital images and if you need any help with your tractor or restoration, I am always happy to advise, as I am also a steam and tractor owner myself.

Peter Love seen in his Triang car, which took part in a couple of 1950s' Paddock Wood, Kent, carnivals, both led by 1911 Burrell Showman's engine 3285 *King George V*.

Seen on 8 February 2012 is 21 year old Emily Burgess at Cross In Hand, near Heathfield, East Sussex, with the family's Muir-Hill 101. It's based on a Ford 5000 skid unit engine, and was originally sold in 1968 by Sussex Tractors of Uckfield. Emily was returning home after retrieving a car that had slid into a ditch. She made full use of the 101's Boughton winch that's fitted on the back.

The 1984 International 1255XL four-wheel drive (ZF axle) had been supplied by Braceys of Bennington who were part of the Delgety Agriculture Ltd Co of the time. It was seen in Hertfordshire on 9 February 2012 at Scott Findley's premises. This former demonstrator had been used with Ransome TS300 ploughs in a push pull set up in its early life.

Perhaps the best loved Huddersfield-made Raspberry Red/Primrose Yellow David Brown is the 990. The Implematic model had excellent grip, which as with any tractor is so important, compared to just engine horse power. This example was bought new by Roland Burgess, who is 86, and was rebuilt by his son Jeff, a very talented engineer. It made its debut at the 2009 Six Bells Bash Boxing Day Road Run that starts from the tractor's original home in East Sussex.

Seen in February 2012 in the snow is Scott Findley, who was called out by Hertfordshire County Council with his Ford 8830 Powershift. Fitted on the front is the Bunce snowplough made near Swindon, which has been a satisfactory implement over the years.

Seen on 26 December 2011 at the charity Larling Angel Road Run held near Snetterton, Norfolk, is Jamie Davey with his 1975 White 2255 (Cockshutt nee Oliver). He had purchased it from the August 2011 Cheffins Harrogate sale and was very pleased with his purchase. It carries the Caterpillar 3150 V-8 engine, which was rather obsolete when fitted in the line but had 126 drawbar horse power with the Over/Under Hydraul-shift transmission that gave 145hp at the pto.

It's 2 February 2012 in Nottinghamshire and I had turned the wrong way as I was heading to Eric Elliott's premises. However, what did I come across in the light snowy conditions, but a 1978 Massey Ferguson 575 with John Deere 140 planter. The two-wheel drive 66hp four-cylinder Perkins A4.236 powered tractor was produced from 1976, with the four-wheel drive version introduced the following year.

Opposite: Having arrived at Eric's premises we had his wonderful 1952 Yeoman of England MK3 tractor out. Turner of Wolverhampton were known for their engineering prowess and their new second generation British diesel tractor was eagerly awaited in 1949 when it was introduced at the Royal Show, which that year was in Shrewsbury. The 'Yeoman of England' tractor was fitted with a hand built marine type V-4 diesel which meant each tractor was slightly different to the next. This example was to sell for £15,250 on 14 April 2012.

The first successful diesel British tractor was the Field Marshall Series One that came along in 1945, replacing the Marshall M. They were relatively popular, made at the famous Britannia Works, Gainsborough, Lincolnshire. Marshall used the single-cylinder line well into the '50s, ending up with the orange Series 3A, which are more collectable in preservation times compared to the Series One here.

Lurking in the woods is the 1961 County Super-4, which of course is based on the Fordson Super Major E1A skid unit. This type of tractor was the beginning of big things for County Tractors Limited at Fleet in Hampshire from its new four-wheel drive twin propshaft system to the front oscillating axle, with its equal sized wheels and tyres.

There were just 197 Marshall MP6 tractors produced. The market for these machines was overseas and offering no implements and hydraulics did not help matters. They had many faults, but the Leyland UE350 six-cylinder engine was one of the better parts. All but ten were sold abroad and 6740057 went in early 1958 to SEDIM in France. They were the most prolific buyer of the MP6 that came to an end in 1961. This older restored example came up at the 14 April 2012 Eric Elliott sale and sold for £40,000.

Opposite: Where do you find a 1977 Massey Ferguson 135 with QD cab 473415 with just five hours recorded on the clock? Well here is an example that the late Nelson Green bought as part of an investment from MF dealer Chandlers of Grantham, Lincolnshire, along with a number of other tractors at the same time. It then came to Eric Elliott and on 14 April 2012 went on to make a record price of £34,000, sold to a very keen Massey Ferguson collector from the Home Counties.

Bob Park has been an avid Massey Harris collector for some years and has also built up the Marsham Rally, near Norwich, which takes place in August, into something very special. Without doubt the star in his collection is the 1951 Massey Harris 55 tandem converted, it is thought, by Alexander Bros of Lockport, Indiana. It worked on the west side of the USA, not far from the Canadian border. It came back to the UK via Indiana in 2009 and after a sort out by Dick Watson, has been a great machine to see at shows in the UK.

This Massey Harris 444 G rowcrop of Bob Park's was photographed in February 2012. The tractor carries the Continual H277cu in engine and replaced the very successful 44 model in 1956. Some 7,393 were to be made and they carry the dual-range transmission. Fitted with a lovely set of Firestone tyres, the tractor is typical of Bob's superb Massey Harris collection and the standard he goes for.

It was in 1892 that Sawyer-Massey was created in Hamilton, Ontario, Canada. Three of the Massey family became involved, but were anti the production of i/c tractors for some reason and moved their money out of the company. Looking back, this was not a wise decision as Massey Harris, such a great implement manufacturer, could have done with Sawyer-Massey to give it a head start in tractor production. This 11-22 model, 5105, was acquired by Bob Park from a 2009 sale in Ontario and was shipped to the UK. It certainly drives well and does all that it should: the author tested it himself in early 2012.

Opposite: Again caught on camera in late February was Chris Rowberry, who along with his younger brother and father have built up one of the best IHC collections in the UK, based in Worcestershire. The 1942 Farmall A is a 2010 restoration and an award winner at Tractor World Malvern, the largest early season tractor indoor show. I created Tractor World in 2001, but because of the Foot and Mouth outbreak it didn't get going until 2002; however it's still continuing to grow ten years later.

I had a call from Cheffins to tell me that well known Chepstow Claas dealer Harold Johns had entered his comparatively rare 1976 John Deere 2030 Mk2 mechanical four-wheel drive tractor in the February Bristol Vintage Sale. This 2130 Mk2 carries the ZF mechanical front axle, not the unreliable hydraulic/electric system that was more widely available on these tractors at the time. I had the opportunity to road test the tractor, with its Duncan cab, that went on to make a record price of £8,200 plus VAT at the Bristol sale.

In late February I was able to catch up with Gary Pepper by Brantham Church just by the River Stour, near Colchester. The 12 January 1955 Ferguson TEA 429800 (straight petrol) was sold by Williams of Colchester. Having just three months to restore it, due to an imminent premises move, it was a pressure job from beginning to end. However the end result on this, Gary's first restoration, is phenomenal and the TEA has won countless awards wherever it has appeared.

The Doe Triple-D are evocative tractors, you either like them or you hate them and on 2 January 2012 I was in Essex to take this picture of Trevor Pagham's 10 September 1964 New Performance example. It's as original as you can find them. Supplied new to J Smith of Great Lodge, Great Bardfield, Essex. Then in 1976 Trevor acquired the Doe with the intention of converting the dual powered machine back into a pair of Fordson NP Super Majors, but the other person involved in the project dipped out. However Trevor used the tractor for just one season and has since carefully stored it outside.

Some 23 Does got together on 31 March – 1 April 2012 at the Norfolk Showground, Norwich, as part of the inaugural Eastern Counties Vintage Tractor & Heritage Show. The oldest to survive, of the George Pryor inspired design, of two Fordson E1A Major tractors together that Does of Ulting went on to manufacture, is Richard Fenton's example 6730 of 1958. It was first seen having been restored by its previous owner in Norfolk, at Tractor & Machinery's Tractor Millennium at Newark Showground where some 1,923 veteran, vintage and classic tractors came together in June 2000 to celebrate the new century.

Trees are the feature, with these pictures on pages 26 and 27, both taken at Bodle Street Green, East Sussex, England, just behind the cottage where Jayne and I live today. On 20 April, the 1990 Case IH 5140 Maxxum with Kverneland rotovator was preparing the fields for the planting of the maze. The 5.9 litre 108hp four-wheel drive tractor had been a reliable beast working on an extensive dairy farm operation run so well by the Van der Meer farming family. Sadly the Maxxum was to be replaced by a John Deere product later in the year.

Opposite: Continuing on the theme of trees, we feature Southover Contractors of Winters Farm Etchingham, which is run by Andrew Madeski. They are using a 2003 New Holland TS115 and Gaspardo six-row planter. The owner told me the tractor had been rather frustrating with an uncomfortable foot throttle position and lots of electrical gremlins, something that was not confined just to this TS115. However now, nearly ten years old, the TS115 is a better performer than in its early days. By lunch time the three fields were all planted ready for the growing season to commence here in East Sussex.

Veteran tractors of this calibre are hard to find and the 1911 International Harvester Co Titan D 25hp XB1193 was seen on 14 April 2012 in Texas while at Lou Buice's birthday party gathering. Restored in Ohio by the famed Wendell Kelch, many thousands of dollars have been spent on XB1193, even down to the IHC tool box locks. The model was made 1910-14 and some 1,757 were produced. At the event Lou started the tractor.

In contrast to the 1911 D, just a few days later at Grandview I came across this International 4366 right by a flea market, indicating the tractor might be for sale. By the looks of it, it had been lying around for some years. This machine was part of the first IHC artic tractor line as such and made 1973-75. This was before the Steiger tie-up between both companies. Engine wise the 4366 carries an International turbocharged six-cylinder diesel of 366 cu in, that produced 167hp and a ten-speed transmission that was capable of a 'heady' 20mph.

Saturday 23 April 2011 saw a raft of road runners from the Republic of Ireland, led by Tony Doyle, arrive at Pembroke Dock to start the Easter Day National Vintage Tractor Road Run. This was to be organised so well by Henry Dixon and his Pembrokeshire crew who raised many thousands for charity. Crusher 'King' Barry Coleman brought over his wonderfully well restored 1980 Ford 7700 that was found at Houghton Hall, Norfolk, with less than 3,000 on the clock. The Deluxe Q-cab was an excellent sound proof fitment on the range at the time.

Taken on 12 May 2012 at Iron Hill Farm Hollycombe, near Liphook on the West Sussex/Hampshire border. We see possibly the leading UK steam boiler-maker, David Bicknell, a former Watson and Haig tractor apprentice of the '80s. David has continued with his tractors and the Ford TW-10 is very much part of the fleet today. As for the Ford 'Hybrid' that started off as a Ford Force 5000 'look alike' it gained a different two-wheel drive front axle, before being turbocharged and gaining a four-wheel drive system. The tractor has been with David for nearly 28 years.

'Still Resting' is perhaps the best term for these next pictures, taken on 3 April in poor light conditions near the Bay of Plenty in the North Island of New Zealand. Many of the vintage and veteran tractors survived in New Zealand owing to the fact that scrap was worthless until the late 1950s, when the Japanese started to move in (now it's the Chinese). Seen upside down is a Fordson F, the first unit cast constructed tractor of its type in the world.

Another spotted in the same yard in New Zealand is this Cleveland. They were known for manufacturing mighty trenchers for many years and using International power units from the T-6 crawler type unit, as used in World War Two and so on. This example has been split, but it's been saved from scrap at this stage at least. Many of these power units have not run up many hours and that makes them desirable for other applications in the preservation world.

County CFT crawlers were popular machines in the late 1940s and early 1950s and were exported extensively through many parts of the UK's former colonial empire. Based on the Fordson E27N Major, this example carries the Perkins P6 TA engine, which really put Frank Perkins' company on the map. By 1959 Perkins had been sold to Massey Ferguson and today is owned by Caterpillar. The cylinder head has been removed on the P6 engine, which was known for cracking high up on the cylinder block.

Organizing an event of the calibre of the Easter Day National Vintage Tractor Road Run is a great responsibility, especially as it moves around the United Kingdom each year. Some are better than others and that's the way it is always going to be, with the weather and different organisers involved. The Henry Dixon 2010 Pembrokeshire event was, however, outstanding with over 800 tractors taking part, as can be seen here just minutes before the action was to start. This was a 25 mile run that had a brilliant lunch stop incorporated, another essential for any National.

Julian Mousley's Roadless Ford Dexta four-wheel drive is one of fewer than 78 genuine examples made by the company. However the Selene front axle could be retro fitted and was extensively used, particularly in mainland Western Europe and New Zealand. This example sold unrestored for £19,500 at the Raymond Pickering sale in November 2005. It must have cost Julian at least another £10,000 to restore and was finished just hours before the National Road Run, where it was certainly the star tractor.

Seen at Henry Dixon's farm in Pembrokeshire are these regulars on the National. The couple are enjoying their two seater John Deere 70, a type that was developed to replace the G in 1954. The 70 features a 51.49hp diesel engine and V-4 gas starting engine and power steering. This was the first JD diesel rowcrop tractor and the most economic tractor for its time; it had 47.7 drawbar horsepower when tested.

It's 7.50am near Pembroke and the tractors are arriving for the day ahead. A type of tractor that is relatively cheap to buy is the International 434. Parts are still available and good quality at that, so they stand a good chance of fitting properly first time. Made as part of the UK IHC Yorkshire operation from 1966-71 and fitted with the 43hp 2.5 litre BD-154 engine that was economic and started reasonably well at that.

Cathy, as this tractor is known, was made at Bathgate, Scotland and is an early example of this type of Leyland 270 that's a second generation blue Leyland tractor, produced from 1973-76. It's fitted with the 'torquey' 3.8NV four-cylinder 71hp engine, which suffered from electrolysis to the liners (eating the liners away through an electric charge). The tractor here has been well restored and a number were built without cabs, although by 1973 all tractors required safety cabs or safety apparatus. Seen at the halfway point of the National.

Owning a Ford 7000 is something very special and out of the 1000 series tractors, the 1971-introduced 7000 is the one to have. One must not forget it is the first turbocharged Ford-engined tractor, basically a 5000 four-cylinder with a Garrett turbocharger that gave 94hp. Another major feature on the 7000 is the Load Monitor sensing, which in its working days could be rather fragile to say the least. So if thinking of buying a 7000, always check this out if you can and the turbocharger as well.

Seen at Tractor World Ireland was the John McGann 1957 Ferguson FE-35 diesel. It was to be runner-up at the show and similarly in its class at Tractor World Malvern in March 2012. Getting the copper/gold colour right is not easy nor is spraying it on without some experience. Seen on the tractor is Maksin Kalinin who has done much of the graft in the restoration of this tractor that looks perfection.

If you want originality then you have got it here with Victor Bryan's 'baby' unstyled John Deere L. The model started out as the Y in 1936, then the 62 and eventually the L line came along in 1937. It was made unstyled to 1938, when it was replaced by a Dreyfuss-styled version, fitted with John Deere's first upright two-cylinder engine that produced 10.42hp from the side-valve 934cc engine and seen at Tractor World Ireland.

Connor Hurley is a prominent owner/restorer and an engineering company owner too. His County Super-6 made its debut at Tractor World in 2011 and has a high class paint finish by P J Savage from Cork City. It's based on the Fordson Super Major skid unit that was beefed up somewhat by County with their own four-wheel drive system, but again utilizing Ford parts. To finish the package off you had the Ford 590E six-cylinder engine, all at a cost of £2,180, in October 1964.

The early May Bank Holiday weekend sees the Tractor World Show Ireland show take place at Corrin Mart, Fermoy, County Cork. It's a very popular show and Jim and Jamie Barron from Dungarvan, County Waterford are avid tractor restorers. Their latest restoration, seen on 2 May 2012, is this Ford Force 3000 narrow that worked for many years in a monastery. Getting the details right on any restoration is so important and owing to not finishing the tractor until the day before the show the dynamo/fan cover had not been fitted.

Opposite: May is a good month for tractor sales and one company that's involved in this is South Eastern Marts. Roger Walters is the main auctioneer here, who is seen in full action on a warm Saturday afternoon near Billingshurst, West Sussex. Roger was to set a UK record auction price for a Fordson Standard N waterwasher (1932-37) at over £4,000. The sales market across the UK is very buoyant and sales are one of the best places to find a restoration project, or a restored tractor.

On a rather damp Saturday 17 September 2011 in Suffolk, we see Tony Donovan from Heathfield bid for the late Peter Fordham 1942 Roadless Traction Company Fordson N that sold at £14,000. The crawler made by this famous Phillip Johnson company was missing its wings, but was essentially a good machine at this Cheffins-run auction.

In 2012 we saw the Woolpit Rally in Suffolk move back to 26-27 May to save it clashing with HM Queen Elizabeth's Diamond Jubilee celebration weekend. The organisers of Woolpit did the right thing as they had tremendous weather. Motor ploughs were the feature and the most successful type worldwide just had to be the Moline Universal C that was imported into the UK by British Empire Motors South Kensington (left). The next generation of tractor is the West brothers of Canterbury, Kent, ex Gary Parker, Indiana sale 1919 Hart-Parr 30.

Not far from Uckfield in East Sussex, working away loading some logs one bright and sunny evening in late May 2011 was this excellent condition and very unusual to see, Massey Ferguson 400 crawler. Fitted with the six-cylinder Perkins A6.354 85fhp engine with torque converter drive and Drott 4 in 1 bucket that was made by Rubery Owen, Darlaston, Staffordshire. Massey Ferguson had success in the UK with the smaller 244 crawler starting in 1963. However when it came to the next decade things did not take off for the company crawler wise.

Late May and Tony Macer is seen in Cambridgeshire with his 1975 John Deere 2130 Series One that had been supplied by Christian Dobbs Ltd of Long Sutton. The glorious weather was used to its best and the tractor was fully road tested. Tony removed the Duncan cab and fitted clamb shell fenders on this well equipped tractor, which even features a trailer lighting socket. The 75hp German-built tractor was perhaps underrated compared to the more popular Ford 5000/5600.

The feature at the 2011 Belvoir Castle Rally in Rutland in May was Ferguson – Massey Ferguson and there was an excellent selection for all to see and enjoy from the AGCO family (Allis Gleaner Corporation). Its 2680 model was made at the Beauvais northern France factory and featured a Perkins 6.354 with turbocharged engine, making the tractor a 130hp machine. It was built 1982-5 and was available in two and four-wheel drive configurations.

Early June sees the Republic of Ireland Bank Holiday weekend and if you are interested in agricultural machinery, there is only one place to head for and that is the Innishannon Rally that started out as the Upton Rally in the 1970s. The scenery is beautiful in this part of County Cork and attending this rally is like going back 40 years. On Monday 3 June 2012 the weather was good and enabled Phillip Green to bring his excellent selection of David Brown tractors to the show, including his ex Vic Mathers from Scotland restored VAK1.

While waiting to catch my plane home from Cork to Stansted, England I was able to visit a collector of original classic tractors. One such tractor was this Massey Ferguson 100 series 188, the ultimate in the range. MF Multi-Power was standard, as were wheelweights and many other items on the 1972-76 made tractors. Produced mostly as two-wheel drive the Four Wheel Traction Co produced official four-wheel drive versions, as well as kits.

It was in 1975 that the Ford 600 series replaced what has become affectionately known as the 1000 series. Our picture clearly shows the new style grille and design compared to the previous range placed in the middle here. The example nearest the camera carries the original type of French Kleber radial tyres and the 1976 Q-cab (bubble) – this was an excellent product and in some ways ahead of its time compared to others, but expensive to make. The cab was manufactured by GKN Sankey Ltd who did well with Ford, but not with MF at the time.

Newby Hall near Ripon, Yorkshire holds an excellent tractor rally in June organised by the Yorkshire Vintage Association. It's different to most commercial rallies and is held in excellent surroundings. Seen on 10 June 2012 is this Roadless four-wheel drive IHC 634 fitted with the BD-281 66hp engine, which was made 1968-72. County also offered the All Wheel Drive version of the 634 with equal wheels.

Opposite: Early June 2011 saw me at a local sale near Cullompton, Devon before travelling on to meet Brian Slater, a tractor and photography fan all his life, at Upton in Payhenbury. Thanks are due to Mark Disney who provided encouragement and great help to Brian and made his life so much easier tractor wise, as they restored a 1967 Massey Ferguson 165 together. Others also helped, including MF 'guru' George French. The end result on a cold and snowy 18 December 2010 after some 15 months' work was something to see, as was the look on Brian's face when he drove the 165, without tin work, down the road and into the fields. With the panels all restored and fitted back on, having done it right as only Brian knows, his Massey Ferguson has given him a new lease of life and some great new friends in the area, from the postman to the local butcher.

Perhaps the most iconic British-built International of all has to be the B-450 that came on line in 1958 at Doncaster. This time IHC had got itself together over the hydraulics which were now internal and worked well. The BD264 engine was good and gave, 57hp. The example here has recently been brought back to life with a replacement cylinder block, after suffering liner problems and was photographed on Saturday 16 June 2012 at Hoath, Canterbury, Kent, thanks to the Johncock family.

While photographing the previous page IHC B-450 I came across this 'hybrid' Allis Chalmers WD that had been brought in from Belgium during preservation times. It originally landed in mainland Europe via the post-war regeneration Marshal Plan. However along the way the WD has gained a four-cylinder Fordson D Series diesel truck engine, besides many other modifications. These include using the D series air tank that's been turned on its end and is now used as an oil reservoir for the improvised hydraulic system.

Weddings are an area where preserved tractors come into their own and that was the case when keen Ford 1000 series owner Rodney Broadley married Zoe Dudman at the delightful Lyminge Parish Church, near Folkestone, Kent, on Saturday 16 June 2012. The 450 guests even travelled behind some of Rodney's fleet, including the Ford Pre Force 5000. The new model was introduced to the public in late 1964 and was put on sale in 1965. Despite various problems the Ford 1000 series was an instant success, even more so in 1968 when the new Force models hit their stride.

Having arrived on his Ford Dexta 2000, Rodney and Zoe left the church behind his 1965 Ford Force 3000. Rodney surprised his bride by dressing as Wurzel Gummidge with his best man as Aunt Sally. Zoe's father, who gave her away, was dressed as The Crowman. The characters of course being made famous by the 1980s' television series that was based on the books by Barbara Todd.

Pictured in June 2012 is the Gordon Carson and Bryan Beba late type IHC Titan 10/20; they have a wonderful collection of tractors in East Anglia. The International 10/20 was a popular tractor in Great Britain during World War One, with over 3,000 of them working in the country. Made at the Milwaukee Works some 78,363 of this two-cylinder model were manufactured 1915-22, but by the end a plough had to be given away to sell them, technology and the Fordson F having moved things on.

One of the best tractors of the 1920s was the 1923-introduced International 10/20 that certainly became a winner straight off and put the Fordson F back in its box. It had been developed from the earlier 8-16 Junior with overhead valves and roller bearing crankshaft that made it something modern and a reliable performer, with a solid cast frame. However, the 10/20 was a smaller version of the 1921-introduced 15/30. In Europe the 10/20 was the big hit and was in production until 1939.

Back at Newby Hall in June 2011 we saw three mighty veteran prairie tractors together, all imports to Europe in preservation times, lining up from left to right. Possibly the noisiest veteran tractor made was the two-cylinder 1912 IHC Titan D 27-45hp. TN647 was built at the Milwaukee works and was a type made 1911-14 and now lives in Yorkshire. Next door is Sjef, Chris and Gijs Koolan's 1924 Aultman-Taylor 30-60 4340 from The Netherlands. This was the most powerful tractor for its time when tested at Lincoln, Nebraska. The last of the big three is the 1915 Twin-City 40-65 1418; some 13 are known to exist today.

Seen in sticky ground conditions at Newby Hall, Yorkshire is the unique to Europe c1924 Bryan steam tractor that was made at Peru, Indiana which was making its UK mainland debut. In fact amazingly some eight examples have survived in this last ditch attempt to use high pressure steam to produce a successful steam tractor. The two-cylinder 20hp engine has a 4 x 5in bore and stroke engine and uses a 600psi multi-water tube boiler.

Opposite: While on the border of Essex and Suffolk in June I was able to call on Gary Pepper and view his latest restoration. It takes the form of a 1944 Fordson Standard N Utility model and after warming the tractor up on petrol it was turned to run on vaporising oil. As it ticked over that wonderful smell this fuel gives wafts over. I was lining up the tractor to the Canon D5 camera when we were joined by a collie sheep dog who wanted to join in the fun.

In Davenham, Cheshire, at Alan and Margaret Davies' premises we caught up with Les Davies and his 1967 Ford Pre Force 3000 HED134E, that has travelled in preservation from Cheshire to Benidorm, Spain and back. Originally supplied to Mr and Mrs Parker of Pear Tree Farm, Acton Bridge, Northwich, Cheshire, it was bought and restored by John Barnes, a former ICI worker of many years.

Peter Stevenson wanted a challenge and he got it quite frankly when he purchased, via eBay, this 1936 John Deere A General Purpose 425729 unstyled rowcrop tractor. It had been a preservation import and came from Scunthorpe, Lincolnshire. It was basically a heap that needed a lot of work to get it right, from a crankshaft regrind upwards. It was to be a three-year project that was successfully concluded at the June 2011 Hadlow Down Rally, East Sussex where the tractor was critically acclaimed.

Seen at the traditional Ardingly rally, held on the South of England Showground, is Oliver West with his 1942 Oliver 80 Standard, one of his first restorations and a prize winner at that. This model was popular during World War Two owing to Lend Lease arrangements and introduced many farmers to internal combustion tractors. As for the 80 it was made from 1937 until the Fleetline series was introduced in 1948.

The unique 1935 Fowler Gyrotiller 170 20681 was one of 66 produced and rebuilt by the late John Clark who paid over £2,000 to buy it from Wards in the '70s. The 170 was then sold to the late John Moffitt and became the focus of the Stapehill Collection at Verwood, Dorset, before being sold to the late Tom Wheatcroft of Donnington Park fame. It has since been sold on again to owners in Yorkshire and was seen publicly for the first time this decade at Newby Hall in poor light conditions on 9-10 June 2012.

John Fowler offered the N C Storey patented rotary hoe device on the back of a number of its crawlers, in various sizes and called them Gyrotillers. Although very successful on virgin land and in sugar cane production, the system brought up the subsoil and even worse clay and wrecked various farming fields as Fowler demonstrated its new product as a replacement to steam tackle in the late 1920s and '30s.

Terry Barnsley of Binley, East Midlands is seen working with his 1960 Caterpillar D8 H 22A with Onions scraper box behind. He was redeveloping some land for a neighbour and was very much recreating how the M1 motorway network was created with similar machinery. This Glasgow-made Caterpillar features direct-drive (six-speed transmission) to the 235 flywheel horsepower turbocharged engine, fitted of course with the double-reduction final drives that became a feature of these machines.

Ian Gibson from Essex is a prolific user of classic Caterpillars. This extensive operator/fitter does a great job rebuilding these machines for another life. No more so than 7 miles from the Dartford Tunnel on the Essex/Kent border where Ian won a contract to remove a large quantity of sand. He used two Caterpillars, a D8H and K, that did the job successfully with a Caterpillar 463G scraper bowl in tow.

Opposite: Rallying can be fun and a tractor that first appeared in 2007 at Ardingly is this totally original condition Eskilstuna, Sweden-made Bolinder-Munktel BM10. The early Saturday evening sunshine gave us a chance to capture this tractor at its best. These 23hp Bolinder W3 twin-cylinder 2.5 litre two-stroke diesel engine tractors were introduced in 1947 and some 6,400 were made by 1952.

Bolinder-Munktells came out with its new model in 1944, the GBMV-1 later to be called the BM-20 after World War Two. It had five-speeds and was capable of 16kpm. Tony Clark is a very skilled intelligent engineer who has lots of experience with Bolinder marine engines and was ideally suited to sort out the complicated BM two-stroke diesel engine. In 1950 BM was bought outright by Volvo who made a similar tractor to the BM-20, the T-21, which used a petrol four-cylinder engine and of course was painted red.

Wrecks like this make a rally something special. This late type 1950s' Caterpillar D4 was seen at the special crawler display at the three-day Kent County Show at Detling, Kent July 2011. The author has commentated at this event for 33 years and thanks to pioneers Richard Pearce and William Day there has always been an excellent tractor, steam and commercial vehicle entry here.

Patina-style tractors like this 1936 Case C are what collectors are looking for more and more today. You can use the tractor in whatever way you want, without spoiling its feel and condition. If you look at the radiator header tank you can clearly see the original paintwork. The Case C was a solid conservative little tractor and was the number three seller in Britain during the 1930s, replaced in 1939 by the Flambeau-styled D.

There is one rally that is a 'must' to attend in Europe and that is the HMT Show at Penningen, The Netherlands at the end of July. There are over 2,000 plus tractors and implements at this event. In addition there are working areas here and much more, although this show has changed over the years and there are not so many early tractors now. However, Lanz is certainly number one and the oil cooled 22/28 hp was the largest production Manheim-made Lanz tractor 1926-31.

Although the weather was gloomy with some rain in 2011, the HMT Show tractors make it all worthwhile. Herman Florissen brought along his unbelievable 1949 Deutz F8M. It has been retro fitted with a mighty eight-cylinder Deutz diesel engine. The tractor started off being based on the F3M417 model that was made 1942-52. It was in 1927 that the German manufacturer Deutz entered the world of tractors with the MTH 222, which looked very much like an earlier Lanz HL 12hp. The company had great connections with Nicolaus August Otto of four-stroke fame (1832-1891).

Set to be the top AGCO award winner at the August Crompton Rally in Derbyshire 2011 is pioneer preservationist Derek Mellor who takes his wonderful Ferguson Brown A 129 around the parade ring. The tractor has lived in Derbyshire all its life and was bought new with 128, which was unfortunately scrapped. It was in 1973 that the tractor came on the scene and ERA 160 is as popular as ever.

Opposite: Curtis and Co of Lewis supplied this 1963 Track-Marshall 55 of John Millam, which was rescuing a 1903 Burrell 2575 6hp single-crank compound Buller. Unfortunately the engine broke its rear axle, of all things, in the parade ring at Ardingly in 2011. The Boughton winch made at Amersham, Buckinghamshire by a company who were originally steam contractors, powered the traction engine back onto the lowloader of Ian McConachie and it was taken away by his 1973 Scammell Handyman. The Burrell is safely back on the road again.

Wheel Horse were pioneers in garden machinery in the 1950s. They were started by Cecil Pond and his son in 1946 with walk away type machines, but they created a four-wheel machine in 1947. The significant R-J58 came along in 1958 and could be fitted with a lawn mowing deck, which Wheel Horse developed more than any other manufacturer at the time. In 1986 the company became part of Toro and sadly the Wheel Horse name is just a memory, it having been dropped from 2007.

Powering its way around the Derbyshire parade ring is the New Generation Waterloo, Iowa-made 1963-66 John Deere 4020 standard. It was voted 'Tractor of the Century' by readers of *Tractor & Machinery* in 2000 and they might be right, particularly when it comes to style and looks. Fitted with a six-cylinder 94hp engine it was well ahead of its time.

Seen in the heart of Shropshire late August is this Ferguson TEA with Clyde Product tilting cab made by Innes Walker Engineering, Paisley, Scotland. The Jersey was very much the standard milking cow in Great Britain and the Republic of Ireland some 50 years ago. The tractor is part of a dedicated Ferguson collection that is just excellent.

Early August in Derbyshire, when I was able to visit Peter Hensen and his Minneapolis-Moline UDS diesel. I arrived early in the evening as the tractor was driven out of its shed, after a very extensive restoration by the owner, helped by many people including Derek Mellor. As the first MM diesel as such, the D283-4 engine had its problems and is fitted of course with American Bosch injection equipment. This excellent example has since been sold to the West Country.

Not all veteran tractor collectors are keen on the Fordson F, basically because it's so common. However saying that, restoring one is a very, very difficult thing to do and getting it right can be so difficult. Many were modified over the years; however here is a late F example looking the part and having a great feel to it at the Crompton Rally on Sunday 7 August 2011.

Presenting a tractor correctly is a hard job to do these days with original style tyre patterns not so readily available and modern designs can certainly spoil the looks. This example, seen at Crompton in 2011, has what it takes and is not over done. The Fordson Diesel E1A was a natural winner for a type of tractor that was ahead of all the opposition in its class. It brought many sales back to Ford, after a slight lull owing to the grey menace in the form of the Ferguson.

Saturday 13 August 2011 found me at Greyabbey, Ards Peninsula, County Down, Northern Ireland, for the County Down's annual working event. Ken Cooke and family put in so much hard work to create a superb County/Roadless/Muir Hill four-wheel drive special. Making its debut at the event was Michael Kirkpatrick's 1980 County 1184TW which featured 128hp under the bonnet. On the back end was the Lempkin 7-furrow semi-reversible plough.

Opposite: Part of the Cooke tractor collection in Northern Ireland and going well at Greyabbey is the Muir Hill 171, the ultimate for many, featuring the Perkins V8.540 and introduced in 1975 giving you a mighty 170bhp under the bonnet. By 1978 the 171 series III had came along, with a little more power from the engine at 177bhp. But time was up for the company as such in 1982. The receivers kept things going until 1984, when fork-lift manufacturer Saunderson took over.

In the other field at Greyabbey the weather cleared for a while, allowing the harvesting to begin and one of the features was a trailed Scandinavian Aktiv combine in such excellent original condition, pulled by a late Massey Ferguson 135 QD cabbed Banner Lane, Coventry-made machine.

County's were the stars at the Greyabbey working, as I tried to contend with taking photographs in one hand, commentating in the other and keeping the rain off the camera lens. I just about juggled all three and it was great to see five Ford derivative four-wheel drives taking to the hill.

Just a few days later I was in Indiana, USA with our Great American Shows Tour P2, which took us to the Maumee Valley Antique Show as our first port of call. Here we were all made welcome and we came across Mark and Roger Schuller's 1913 J I Case 20-40 1987. It's one of 4,263 made and had been stored in a shed that had come down around its ears, after some 60 years.

Opposite: Just a few yards away from the Case was the top of the range 1961 Ford 901 with Ford's ten-speed Select-O-Speed semi-automatic power-shift transmission and three-point linkage. This was a troublesome piece of engineering, which few understood and still don't. It's fitted with the hard to find Ford four-furrow semi-mounted plough. Owned and restored by Dave Van Tilburg who has done an excellent job.

Advance-Rumely OilPull was the 'king' of early prairie tractors made at LaPorte, Indiana. The OilPull refers to the cooling, which is by oil, not water, and is very practical in the low winter temperatures. The G 20-40 is seen at the Mid Michigan Old Gas Tractor Association excellent show on 19 August 2011 which was hosting the Advance-Rumely Club Expo.

Certainly rare to see is the Aultman-Taylor 15-30, restored by professional restorer Justin Click of Gary, Indiana for George Scharf, Chicago. Photographed near Owosso, Michigan as part of the Mid Michigan Show, this was Aultman-Taylor's only lightweight tractor type that featured the Climax four-cylinder engine and was marketed from 1918-24 when the company was taken over at Battle Creek by Advance-Rumely.

At Monticello, Illinois we were able to take in a Nixon Auctioneers sale. Here Bryan and Grace Beba were lucky enough to be able to buy the Rock Island Heider D 9-16 Friction Drive tractor, in fully restored condition. This model was made by the Illinois company from 1916 until amazingly, 1929. In fact this actual tractor had lived inside, as it worked in a saw mill all its life under cover. It arrived in the UK in early December and runs a treat, now based in East Anglia.

Collecting tractors has been very much part of Scott Zoborosky's life in Indiana and it's also very much part of his son's life, as he drives the late type unstyled John Deere DI that's been perfectly restored by this family. It was 1935 when John Deere introduced its industrial version of the D. It started at number 120029 and they only made 100 DIs by the time the unstyled model was dropped in 1941 at 150118.

The ultimate tractor when it comes to collecting just has to be the 1938 Minneapolis-Moline UDLX. This go anywhere tractor had a high enough road speed that you could go shopping with it and had a radio and cigarette lighter as standard. The UDLX can't be described as a great success; about half of the 150 survive today and sell for, in good order, £120,000. This example was seen at the Nixon Auctioneers Ruth Ann Shrock Auction Sale in late August 2011.

We see Leigh Miles from Herefordshire testing a 1963 Minneapolis-Moline Jet Star 2 Diesel, a type only made for one year. It carries the D206-4 engine on a type of tractor that was not popular for the company. The line-up of tractors that were to be offered the next day here was certainly typical of what is found at various sales in the Mid-West of North America.

Big power comes in all forms, as seen at the Half Century of Progress Show at Rantoul, Illinois, at the former Chanute USAF airbase. Here we see the wildly talented *Heritage Iron* editor Sherry Schaffer aboard the Kinze 8850 dual engined 12-cylinder John Deere. It features two Cummins 855 engines that are coupled together with a high-speed silent chain.

Jon Kinzenbaw brought along his 1971 creation in the form of Kinze Old Blue, to the Half Century of Progress, fitted with dual power 640hp GM V-8 Detroit engines in the monster artic tractor. It was originally created to demonstrate the Kinze licensed to DMI 12-furrow Hydra-Wide plough that had also been totally rebuilt and placed on the back end.

One of the major features at the Half Century of Progress is the corn harvesting and there were 141 corn pickers working. IHC were number one in the USA and Canada when the 1951 Farmall M rowcrop was made. As for the 1969 Farmall 544 rowcrop diesel on the right, well that was available with hydrostatic power steering, live hydraulics and category two three-point hitch.

Working away through the crop picking the corn on the cob with the cutter bar on the other side of the tractor, is the 1959 John Deere 530 rowcrop. It was offered in three fuel versions with the gas version of the two-cylinder engine seen here giving 38.58 bhp. It would be just one more year before the John Deere New Generation multi-cylinder in-line range would revolutionise people's thinking.

Planes and people were very much part of the site at Rantoul and the 1958 Massey Ferguson 50 gas with two-furrow plough was going for it. The lady was concentrating on where she was going, rather than the ploughing standard, but I am sure she was having a fine time in great weather conditions.

Opposite: Ed McLaughlin of McLaughlin Farms, Manhattan, Illinois was making a real go of it on the Sunday morning of the Half Century of Progress. He was using his 1962 John Deere 4010 rowcrop 80hp diesel to good effect. Fitted with Synchro-Range transmission, the Waterloo ten series was far superior to the Dubuque-made products which encompassed the smaller end of the range.

It's evening time and everyone is off to feed their faces or watch the tractor pull at the Rantoul-based show. We came across the superbly restored 1912 Emerson & Brantingham Gas Engine 4 owned by Little Log House Pioneer Museum in Hastings, MN. It had originally been preserved by John Tissie of South Dakota.

The 1959 Ford 971 Select-O-Speed tri-cycle rowcrop carries the 172 cu in gas engine and has rear wheel studs for the fitment of dual wheels. Those Firestone tyres and the Ford 711 One Arm Loader make the Duane Riddle from Rochester, Illinois-owned tractor certainly stand out from the crowd.

All the way from Ohio was the Randall Brothers 1984 Steiger Tiger IV fitted with the Cummins KP-525hp six-cylinder turbocharged 18.9 litre engine. The model was near the end of the line, as the company were to be taken over by Tenneco (IHC owners) just a few years later. Behind the mighty green artic is the Wil-Rich multi-plough.

We moved on to view various other shows and called in to Pontiac, Illinois to see what their show was all about. We were met by the local tourist board representative who presented us with lots of gifts. We came across this 1967 J I Case 1200 Traction King, which of course features four-wheel steering.

As always if you enjoy tractors, visiting an extensive sale yard is all part of the process and that is the case when viewing Polk - McGrew's yard near Warsaw, Indiana. There are normally over 600 antique tractors to enjoy at each of the two annual sales that are held here each year.

Cool orchard tractors are something very special to me. To restore one of these machines, with long fenders designed to protect the tractor and branches of the fruit trees, takes some skill. Most in working times were damaged in more ways than one and making things right is a panel beater's nightmare, but the end result here on this International McCormick O-4 (W-4 really) is outstanding.

Now at the modern day Farm Progress Show at Decatur, Illinois we come across this J I Case 'eyebrow' 830 hi-crop that's been rebuilt as part of a national school tractor competition. It gives students practical hands on knowledge and skill, as they themselves rebuild the machine to rally standard and are sponsored as the job comes together.

Michael Davis gets behind the wheel of the Boomgarden's early type International Harvester Co Mogul 8-16 that came on line during 1914 when some 20 or so were produced. It was never however in the league of the Milwaukee works-made Titan 10-20, with only 14,065 having been made when the model was dropped in 1917 for a larger Mogul 10-20 variant.

Opposite: Seen at the Buckley Show in upper Michigan, where attendance is regularly as high as 54,000, the parade in the afternoon of the show is something else and includes this Cletrac 40. It was made by the Cleveland, Ohio company 1928-31 and featured a Beaver six-cylinder engine. Around 1,600 at best were built of this substantial crawler of the time.

Built in Winnipeg, Canada the Versatile 575 is seen powering its way along on 30 August 2011 at the Farm Progress Show, Decatur, Illinois. Versatile was founded by Canadians Peter Pakosh and Roy Robinson and become the largest producer of articulated four-wheel drive tractors, starting in 1966 with the D100 and G100. Taken over by Ford in the '80s they were then spun off when CNH was formed. The next owner was Buhler Industries who didn't have an easy ride. Today they are owned by the largest combine manufacturer in the world, Rostselmash Inc of Russia.

The Caterpillar Challenger was the world's first rubber-tracked agriculture machine, created in 1987. The MTS design combined the flotation and traction of steel tracks with the versatility of rubber tyres that can increase tractive effort. In 2002 the brand was purchased by AGCO and the Challenger tractors have been manufactured at the company's Jackson, Minnesota facility since. AGCO have added rubber-tyred tractors to the range, mostly Massey Ferguson tweaked and coloured to the Challenger brand.

 In the morning of the Farm Progress Show if the weather is good, there is a corn harvesting session. One that has gradually made headway in the USA since 2001 has been Claas in its Caterpillar joint North American venture. They are based at Grand Island, Nebraska where the machines are assembled having been manufactured at Harsewinkle, Germany and use, of course, Caterpillar engines.

Opposite: New Holland have made great strides as a world manufacturer. The Fargo, North Dakota-built 9 Series T9560 artic comes out of the former Steiger/IHC facility and is pulling a Landell 2130 combination to great effect. These types of artic units are very much a refinement on the dinosaurs that roamed much of the upper part of the USA and the lower part of Canada during the 1970s-90s.

Just two days later on 2 September 2011 I had flown back to the UK and was at The Great Dorset Steam Fair enjoying a cup of tea at 8am. The weather has its ups and downs here and luckily I had struck it right with good weather for photography on the Friday. Seen in the superb working area is the Hampshire-based (all its life) very late Case L, the biggest offered by the company in the 1930s. The next group of pictures were all taken at the Fair.

Seen in Gerald and Mandy Mundy's Tractor Working Section is this 1938 Allis Chalmers UC rowcrop. Dave Everett's example came out of a sale in Oxfordshire that had been cancelled and was held a month later in October 2008. It was sold at a very cheap price for one of these rare machines and is one of five known in the UK.

Even with neck and shoulder problems Derek Mellor was in top form with his 1936 Massey Harris 25 that was making its rally debut. Derek had owned this ex Toddington Manor tractor for nearly ten years. Behind is the Massey Harris two-furrow plough that was a good product by the company.

Herbert Saunderson was a pioneer in British tractor design, but when he finally got some stability with financial backing from the Crossley brothers, he somehow seemed to lose the plot. This Saunderson & Mills G is part of the Smith collection and was working in the threshing area at this the largest show of its type in the world.

Seen in the working section late on Friday evening is the 1940 Caterpillar D8 8R 628 with LeTourneau Carry-all 9 yard scraper bowl behind. This machine owned by Marriott and Tideswell from Buxton, Derbyshire was assigned to the Royal Engineers Armoured Division. It landed on Gold Beach four days after D-Day in Normandy on 10 June 1944. Finding a clean background at The Great Dorset Steam Fair is very difficult these days.

Opposite: Graham Spark comes from a family who have been keen on vintage machinery, especially Fords, for decades. His latest restoration comes in the form of the 1959 Fordson E1A Power Major Triple-D. It's one of the earliest in preservation that was bought from Hampshire as a parts case. Graham has rebuilt the tractor so well that the engines tick over like no other and is a great credit to him.

On Sunday 4 September 2011 I got a call from my good friend Arthur Tingley to tell me he was ploughing with his late type 1947 Oliver 90. This tractor went to work for Luggs of Billingshust, West Sussex, well known agricultural contractors at the time, where it worked with another example. 'Big Ollie' is still in its original clothes and has its ups and downs and on this day had a fuel mixture problem.

Also seen around this time at Onslow Park, Shropshire is Derek Fildes with his 1938 Allis Chalmers WF, which his father owned when just a year old. It was delivered by train to the nearby railway station. The WF took some time for Allis Chalmers to style compared to the WC. When photographed the tractor was debuting at the rally having had an extensive four year restoration.

Buying and selling Fergusons is something that Arthur Tingley did for many years off and on, in-between his extensive farming career. The best loved of all the grey Fergusons has to be the Ferguson TED (petrol/paraffin). This example is typical of what you would see around the farms across the whole of the UK and Republic of Ireland, going about their business.

Some crawlers linger on and nearly die: one such example is this 1956 Fowler VFA the very last type of Fowler (nee Field Marshall) single-cylinder crawler. At the time it was owned by Brian Tompsett and had a 20 year plus restoration just to get the machine back and into running condition. The cylinder block had been extensively cracked when water had been left in the engine one winter (by mistake). Brian was able to bring the VFA back to life with various other people's help.

The red Farmall F-14 was only produced for two years in the late 1930s. A good number came to the UK to be used particularly in East Anglia. Chris Rowberry's example had an extensive restoration to say the least with many parts coming over from North America. It was to be a prize winner straight out the box and was bought at a sale as a pile of parts, for less than £900.

Noted for sale in *Tractor & Machinery* our Essex owner travelled north to obtain what was then an older restored Allis Chalmers D-272, which had been supplied new by S V Milnes of Newark. This was the last in the line of Allis Chalmers Essendine works B derivatives. Carrying the post Perkins P3 diesel engine also made it an alternative to the Massey Ferguson 35 and Fordson Dexta, but made little impact quite frankly.

When the BMC Mini hit the ground in 1966 it was heavily criticized by the press at the time. As with many British Leyland projects it lacked some development, but by the time the Leyland 154 came out the tractor was a good machine. Even having lots of gears the tractor still only does 12-14 mph at maximum. Simon Smart's example certainly looks the part in the late summer sunshine near Ardleigh, Essex.

On 23 September 2011 in Derbyshire I was able to meet up with a tractor I have owned for nearly 14 years. It takes the form of a very rare 1937 Love, which was made at Benton Harbour, Michigan, USA. Jebez Love started making tractors in 1934, called Tructor's. Love was still in business in the 1950s, but by 1955 the tractor line had come to a stop. Today approximately 24 Love tractors survive, with two examples in Europe, both owned by the author.

Seen on 24 September is Ian Brown of Fife, Scotland and his 1935 award winning Fordson Standard N waterwasher. It's been restored for some 10 years now, but looks as good as ever by this well known New Holland dealer. Our picture is taken at the Scottish National Vintage Tractor Show at the Lawrie and Symington's Lanark premises.

On the way back south I was able, on 25 September, to call into Derbyshire where I caught this JCB1 Mk1 at work. It was sorting out the dung heap and was a type of machine that was introduced in 1962 with the 20hp Petter PH two-cylinder engine. As we can see the blade that was part of the package along with the back actor was working well.

ABM Plant Hire are keen on older machines and besides the modern fleet have a number of preserved machines they like to take to shows when time allows. This picture is pure nostalgia with the JCB ID dumper and 1963 JCB Mk1 working together on a small pipeline job.

In contrast on Friday 22 July 2011, I spotted near Willingham, Cambridgeshire on a cloudy evening a 1998 Massey Ferguson 36 combine at work. I had to stop and with permission from the operator, was able to take a set of pictures of its working. Interestingly the combine I believe has been sold on.

Opposite: Little Casterton took place on 17-18 September 2011 and Paul Smith a very experienced John Deere man is driving Ron Knight's former Channel 4 TV series Salvage Squad Massey Harris 780 rebuild. The combine carries a 58hp Perkins L4 engine and has an electrically-operated 10ft header.

Back at Little Casterton, not far from Stamford, we see this International TD-9 crawler that was debuting at the event. The model came along in 1939 and was not that popular in the UK, but some 58,182 were to be made, remarkably, including the T-9 gas version as well.

Opposite: John Deere's A and B rowcrops were seen more in East Anglia than anywhere else when new during the late '30s-'40s. However after World War Two and import duty restrictions new American tractors became a thing of the past. John Deere's reliability has seen a good number of UK original machines preserved along with modern day imports.

This General Motors Samson G was imported by US Tractors and purchased by Alan Ward who then sorted the tractor out. It debuted at the late August Onslow Park event in 2011. One has to say the gearing on the Samson is typical of the period and is rather high to say the least.

Richard Sturdy of Newby Hall fame is seen with his former Peter Bourne October 2009 sale Allis Chalmers 20-40 Thresherman's Special. A very rare machine even in the USA, it is seen at work at Little Casterton where it drank lots of fuel along the way.

One of the pioneers of the preservation movement is Arthur Hinch who is these days a very keen Allis Chalmers fan. He was out working at his own event (Little Casterton) with his ex military Allis Chalmers HD15 which of course featured a GM 6-71 Detroit engine that came on line in 1951.

The ploughing season really gets underway in early autumn and seen on Saturday 1 October 2011 is the next day's Ferguson Club annual ploughing match winner. The match takes place near Bury St Edmunds. The Ferguson FE-35 diesel grey and gold type is known as a hard starter, even renowned engine 'guru' Harry Ricardo had a go at the engine for MF, but it was not any better than before unfortunately.

Well known haulier Phillip Warren has put together a push-pull outfit using his very original County TW 1184 four-wheel drive. The four-furrow Ransomes TS-300 plough on the front was made not many miles away at Ipswich, Suffolk. Ransomes for many years were the largest agricultural manufacturing company in the world.

Opposite: A Massey Ferguson 65 owned by my associate Henry who did such an excellent job organising the Ferguson Club's annual plough match on 2 October. The MF 65 is a much underrated tractor, better balanced than a Fordson E1A Major and excellent traction as well. More examples should have sold at the time from this Banner Lane, Coventry manufacturer.

Down at the 2011 October National Ploughing Championship held in Somerset we see George Allwood. This World ploughman came away with the coveted title of Vintage National Ploughing Champion with his 1960 International B-275. His presentation with red IHC overalls was just right as well, but was using a Ransomes TS-86 plough at the backend.

Colin Turner has been a ploughman for many years, having been involved in farming and transport all his life. The former Sussex Champion has ploughed with Farmall, Fordson, Track Marshall, but has now turned to a Caterpillar D2 and a Ransomes TS-46 and has taken many class awards along the way.

In Bodle Street Green, a village in East Sussex, during World War Two no fewer than two Case LAs worked for John Barnes & Son on contract threshing and sawing. Later on one at least was sold locally to W Keeling. However at Brown Bread Street some 4 miles away from BSG in October we saw a similar example to what John Barnes & Son used all those years ago.

Also caught at Brown Bread Street at the autumn road run is the 1982 David Brown 1490. It was a type sold locally by John Barnes & Sons and also by Curtis & Co of Lewes, East Sussex. The 1490 was a good seller for David Brown and this example is owned by Roy Grinstead, a keen David Brown collector near Heathfield, East Sussex.

Seen at Biggin Hill, Kent the same day in October is this 1950 Fordson E27N Major that has been restored meticulously by its owner, who also runs a famous bodyshop. The Perkins P6 (TA) is very much the ultimate in E27N ownership and can fetch as much as £17,000, as one example did at auction a few years ago now.

October sees us in Worcestershire as I preview an H J Pugh sale that was to take place successfully the following January 2012. This tractor sold for over £2,000 at the sale. The Allis Chalmers B was introduced in 1937 with a Waukesha engine to be followed the following year by Allis' own engine. All Bs pre 1941 carry the bow front axle, like this example. However after World War Two, well that's a different story, but the tractor by then had a straight axle.

Four-wheel drive was to become the future of farming. One such company that pursued this dream was the Italian company SAME, which got into the act in the early '50s. Both these tractors were to come up at the sale in January 2012 and although the example on the left didn't made the reserve, over £3,000 was paid for the 'baby' Sametto on the right.